M000291164

GEOGRAPHY
Riddles and Puzzles

Written by Beth Thompson

Senior Editor: Christine Hood
Editor: Kevin Starnes
Illustrations: Scott Bricker
Inside Design and Production: Rose Sheifer
Cover Design: Rose Sheifer

GOOD APPLE
A Division of Frank Schaffer Publications, Inc.
23740 Hawthorne Boulevard
Torrance, CA 90505

© 1999 Good Apple. All rights reserved. Printed in the United States of America.

Note: Pages may be reproduced for classroom or home use only, not for commercial
resale. No part of this publication may be reproduced for storage in a retrieval
system, or transmitted in any form or by any means—electronic, mechanical,
recording, etc.—without the prior written permission of the publisher. Reproduction
of these materials for an entire school or school system is strictly prohibited.

Contents

Introduction 4

The Five Fundamental Themes
of Geography 5

Word Wackies

States 7

Cities 8

Geography Analogies

United States 9

World 10

Which One Does Not Belong? United States 11

Which One Does Not Belong? World 12

Geography Riddles

Rivers, Lakes, Mountains, and Parks 13

Logic Puzzles

Rivers and States 23

Continents and Islands 25

Cities, Countries, and Continents 26

Volcanoes 28

Answers 30

Introduction

Geography is a subject often thought by students to be boring or irrelevant. It's usually the presentation of the subject, not the subject itself, which leads students to these conclusions. Geography can be presented in a way that is challenging, motivating, and fun, which this book, *Geography Riddles and Puzzles*, aims to do. This resource provides dozens of motivating, high-interest opportunities for students to explore the geography around them as well as the world at large. The activities encourage students to use their left-brain thinking skills (critical thinking, analyzing, logic) in a subject not traditionally thought of as an analytical discipline. By using more left-brain skills in problem solving, students who think more analytically will enjoy geography more than ever, while those who tend to think more "right brain" will find fresh challenges in this different way of thinking about geography.

This book contains four types of activities:
- Word Wackies
- Geography Analogies
- Geography Riddles
- Logic Puzzles

All of these activities require the use of higher-level thinking skills and are designed to interest and challenge students in their thinking toward geography. These activities may be used in a curricular study, or as single enrichment opportunities. Encourage students to use any available maps, globes, and atlases, as well as other geographic resources to help them work the problems. Many of these activities are also effective for working in pairs or small, cooperative groups.

The first section is called Word Wackies. In these activities, students try to figure out each state or city by looking at picture and word clues. If students are not sure of a city or state, they can use an atlas index to see if the name they came up with truly does exist. Remember to allow for answers other than those listed if they seem reasonable or logical, which will encourage analytical thinking.

The second section is Geography Analogies. These activities require students to use a map of the United States and figure out possible relationships. Students will look for the relationship between the first two words. If the first word is a capital city and the second word is the state, then students will write the other missing capital or state. If they find answers other than those given, ask them to explain. If the reasons are logical, accept them.

Geography Riddles make up the third section, which are written in the first person from a geographer's point of view. Students read the clues carefully and determine which geographic structure is being described, such as a mountain or bay, then which specific mountain or bay is being described, such as Mt. McKinley or Galveston Bay. Encourage students to use maps, globes, atlases, and other geography resources to solve these riddles. These activities are also excellent for paired or small-group learning.

The fourth section is Logic Puzzles. In these activities, students match items that go together and cross out those that do not match. The purpose of logic puzzles is to encourage students to read information carefully and make logical deductions based on the information. They will also write "proof statements" to support their conclusions.

All students will benefit from these activities, not only because of their original and creative approach to geography, but also because of the different way they present the subject matter. This unique perspective on geography may possibly open up an exciting new world to students who had previously viewed geography in a negative light.

The Five Fundamental Themes of Geography

Geography

Is the study of the earth,
Of land and sea,
And volcanic birth.

First, there's **Location,**
That is where a place is at,
Located on a map grid
With a longitude and lat.
This absolute location
Involves the earth and sun,
Legends, scales, and globes,
And map projections.
Location can also be
Rather relative,
That's the distance and direction
From the place where I live.
That's the first theme
Of geography;
It's strictly fundamental
To you and me.

The second theme
Is the theme of **Place.**
It's a study of landforms
And the human race,
Of flora and fauna,
Climate and hydrology,
How people make a living,
And the local industry.
Is it a town or a city?
What's the ideology?
Is it a good place to live?
Is it the right place for me?

Human interaction with the air, sea, and land;

The third basic theme
Deals with the world and man,
Excessive pollution
And hazardous waste,
Resulting from greed
And thoughtless haste.
Humans using resources,
Such as timber and coal,
Making high technology
The primary goal.
Building lakes and dams
And patrolling men's pollution,
Conserving and preserving
Are still the best solution.

Movement

Is the fourth theme
In geography.
Voyages of discovery
On the land and sea.
Modes of transportation
Such as plane, rail, and bus,
Migration and trade
And their effects on us.
Global interdependence
And spatial efficiency,
How to get from here to there,
And from sea to shining sea.

The fifth theme is **Regions,**
North, south, east, and west.
Traits they have in common
Help them pass a region's test.
A region may be political,
Landform or climatic,
Religious or ethnic,
Such as Slavic or Islamic.
The corn belt is a region,
And so's the coastal plains,
The Appalachian Mountains,
And the tropical forest
that rains.

Now I know five themes
Basic to geography.
Each one of these themes
Relates geography to me.
So when I look at cities,
Oceans, deserts, and the sea,
I'll have a better sense
Of the subject *geography!*

© Good Apple GA13015

Reproducible

The Fundamental Themes of Geography

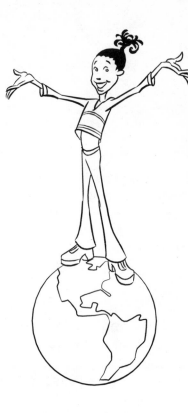

as They Relate to _____
                                    (Your Hometown)

Look up the following information about your hometown in an atlas or other resource and answer the following questions.

1. LOCATION

A. Absolute Location
- What is your present latitude and longitude?
- Within what hemisphere do you live?

B. Relative Location
- What direction are you from the city of Dallas, Texas?
- On what side of your state do you live?

2. PLACE

A. Physical Characteristics
- What types of landforms are near you?
- What is your location's climate? What wildlife and natural vegetation is nearby?

B. Human Characteristics
- What ethnic groups live near you?
- What types of employment and religious ideologies are there?

3. HUMAN-ENVIRONMENTAL RELATIONS

- What physical (human-made) structures are near you?
- How has past economic activity helped or hurt your area?

4. MOVEMENT

- What shopping facilities are located within one mile from you?
- What resources are brought in from other parts of the world?

5. REGIONS

- Within what region of the country do you live, and what are some of the geographic features of your area?
- What other region is close to you? How is it different from yours?

Word Wackies: States

Analyze each picture and try to figure out which state it represents by using the clues in the box.

1.

I'll ask her

2.

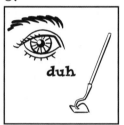

3.

4.

eeeeeeeee
ccccccccc

5.

6.

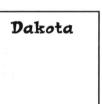

7.

Dakota

8.

9.

I
C   U
    T

10.

11.

Mrs.

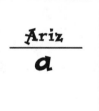

12.

Ariz
___
a

13.

mich   mich

14.

Virginia

15.

ADO

16.

&

© Good Apple GA13015

Reproducible

Word Wackies: Cities

Analyze each picture and try to figure out which world city it represents by using the clues in the box.

1.

son
son

2.

3.

4.

D

5.

AHAc

6.

7.

ramento

8.

9.

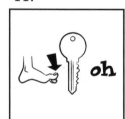

10.

VER

11.

oh

12.

lost wages

13.

14.

15.

+A

16.

Tor

Geography Analogies: United States

Use a United States map to complete these analogies. Then write the relationship below each analogy. The first one is done for you.

The symbol : = *is to*; the symbol :: = *as*.

1. Montgomery : Alabama :: <u>Austin</u> : Texas
   (Or, *Montgomery is to Alabama as Austin is to Texas*)
   Montgomery and Austin are both capitals of their states.

2. Laredo : Rio Grande :: Minneapolis :_____
   _____

3. New Mexico :_____ :: Oklahoma : Oklahoma City
   _____

4. Florida :_____ :: California : Pacific Ocean
   _____

5. Topeka : Kansas ::_____ : Nevada
   _____

6. _____ : Alabama :: Indiana : Illinois
   _____

7. Canada : United States ::_____ : Mexico
   _____

8. _____ : South Carolina :: Richmond : Virginia
   _____

9. Texas : NM, OK, AR, LA :: Maine :_____
   _____

10. Salt Lake : Utah ::_____ : Florida
    _____

© Good Apple GA13015

Reproducible

Geography Analogies: World

Use a world map to complete these analogies. Then write the relationship below each analogy. The first one is done for you.

The symbol : = *is to;*
the symbol :: = *as.*

1. Madrid : Spain :: <u>Paris</u> : France
   (Or, *Madrid is to Spain as Paris is to France*)
   Madrid and Paris are both their country's capitals.

2. Norway : Sweden :: Portugal : _____

   _____

3. Laos : _____ :: Chile : Argentina

   _____

4. _____ : Egypt :: Panama Canal : Panama

   _____

5. Surinam : Guyana, Brazil, French Guiana :: _____
   : Colombia, Brazil, Guyana _____

6. Nepal : China :: _____ : Brazil

   _____

7. Malaysia : Asia :: _____ : North America

   _____

8. South Africa : Africa :: Argentina : _____

   _____

9. Caspian Sea : Asia :: _____ : North America

   _____

10. The Nile : Africa :: _____ : South America

   _____

© Good Apple GA13015 Reproducible

Which One Does Not Belong? United States

Use a United States map to figure out what each group of states has in common, and circle the one that does not belong. Then explain why it does not belong. The first one is done for you.

1. Idaho   Nebraska   Utah   (Iowa)   Montana

All other states border Wyoming.

2. Washington   North Dakota   Maine   New York   Wisconsin

3. Texas   Nevada   North Carolina   California   Oregon

4. Nevada   Colorado   Utah   Arizona   New Mexico

5. Louisiana   New Mexico   Texas   California   Arizona

6. Nebraska   Kansas   South Dakota   Nevada   North Dakota

7. Tennessee   Ohio   Wisconsin   Illinois   Mississippi

8. Georgia   Rhode Island   Alabama   Florida   Massachusetts

9. South Dakota   Utah   Kentucky   Oregon   Wyoming

10. New York   Michigan   Ohio   Vermont   Pennsylvania

Which One Does Not Belong? World

Use a world map to figure out what each group has in common, and circle the one that does not belong. Then explain why it does not belong. The first one is done for you.

1. Brazil   Peru   Ecuador   Chile   (Panama)

   All other countries are in South America.
   _____

2. Argentina   Brazil   Paraguay   Guyana   Uruguay
   _____

3. Zaire   Libya   Somalia   Egypt   Madagascar
   _____

4. North America   Europe   Asia   Africa   Australia
   _____

5. Atlantic   Pacific   Indian   Antarctica
   _____

6. Canada   Mexico   Greenland   Norway   Venezuela
   _____

7. Argentina   Zaire   India   Tasmania   South Africa
   _____

8. Ecuador   Kenya   Borneo   Congo   Vietnam
   _____

9. Tahiti   Hawaii   Philippines   Japan   New Zealand
   _____

10. Arctic   Asia   South America   Antarctica   North America
    _____

Geography Riddles
Rivers, Lakes, Mountains, and Parks

Read the following paragraphs and look for hints to see what place in the world is being described. Then put the clues together and solve each riddle.

1. I was born in the ocean long ago.
   When I'm really active, I "glow with the flow."
   I sit sandwiched between islands near a plate.
   I belch and I burp and I determine others' fate.
   I'm very large—the largest of my kind.
   A sight more spectacular is hard to find!
   WHAT AM I?

   _____

2. Akin to a gulf—in the U.S. I am found.
   I'm also a ria, "a river that's drowned."
   I live on the coast, partly surrounded by land.
   My mouth is wide, and my edges are sand.
   I'm in the Northeast on the Atlantic Coast.
   "I'm the largest one there" is my primary boast.
   WHAT AM I?

   _____

3. I'm skinny and narrow—a fine piece of land.
   Humans dug through me with plans "oh, so grand."
   I divide bodies of water and connect landmasses.
   Through my man-made gorge, a giant ship passes.
   I connect North and South America and two large oceans.
   I can assist or detain man's locomotion.
   WHAT AM I?

   _____

4. I'm a flat, low-lying plain.
Alluvium builds me up after floods from heavy rain.
I'm oddly shaped, like the foot of a bird.
I grow as the river's flow is slightly deterred.
I can be found in the Gulf of Mexico.
Two-hundred million tons a year is how much I grow!
WHAT AM I?

_____

5. I'm part of a landmass—a point of land.
In the Atlantic Ocean, I take my stand.
I'm part of a continent—on the southern tip.
Around my point, there's been many a trip.
I'm in the Southern Hemisphere; I form False Bay.
I jut out in the ocean—I'm in a sailor's way!
WHAT AM I?

_____

6. I'm a major landform, seen around the earth.
When plates collide and wrinkle, I am given birth.
I'm folded, and I am the highest peak.
My pinnacle is the goal many humans seek.
I'm located in Asia—a natural barrier.
I've made many thrill-seekers feel a little bit "warier"!
WHAT AM I?

_____

7. Concrete is the substance from which I am made.
For me, millions of dollars was the price that was paid.
I span the Colorado River, and I'm 726 feet tall.
I'm a man-made structure that looks like a wall.
I control the mighty river and its waters' flow.
I regulate the reservoir behind me—I can make it high or low.
WHAT AM I?

_____

8. I'm a small body of land, and water surrounds me.
Continental drift caused me to break into the sea.
I'm south of the equator in the Indian Ocean.
To the French, I pledge my colonial devotion.
A belt of forest follows my long coastline.
My climate is mostly tropical—my weather is fine!
WHAT AM I?

_____

9. I'm "almost an island," jutting into a sea.
Middle America is where you will find me.
Many people visit me on their holidays.
On my pristine beaches, they like to play!
I have a long coastline and an interesting history.
For years my Mayan ruins have been a mystery!
WHAT AM I?

_____

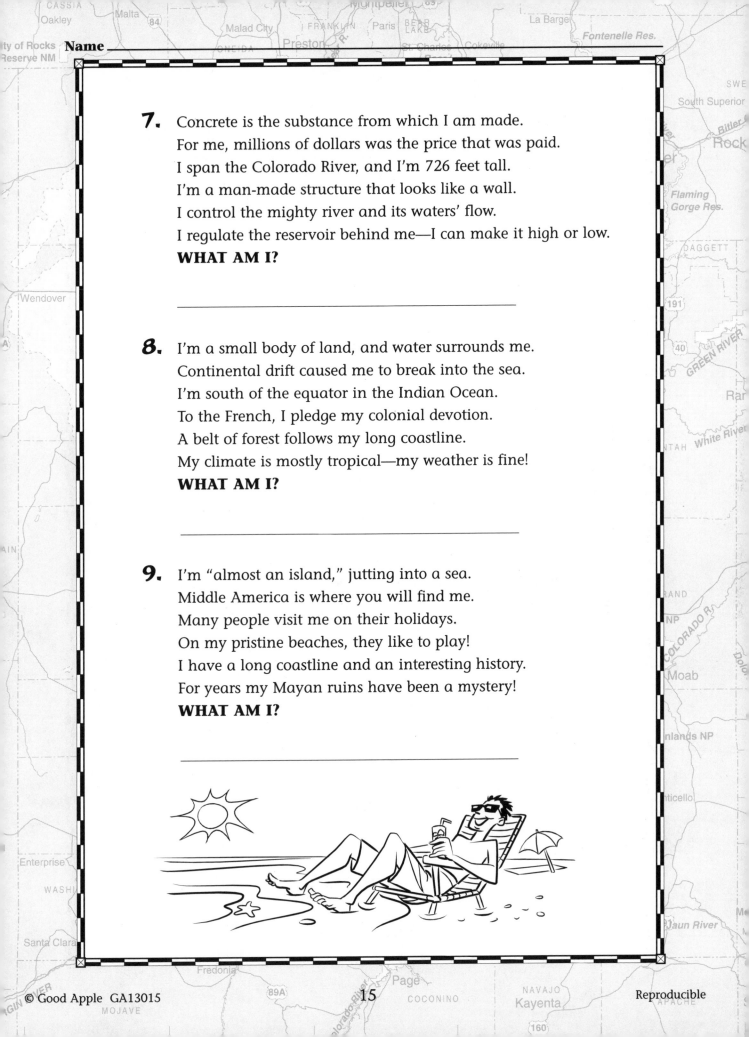

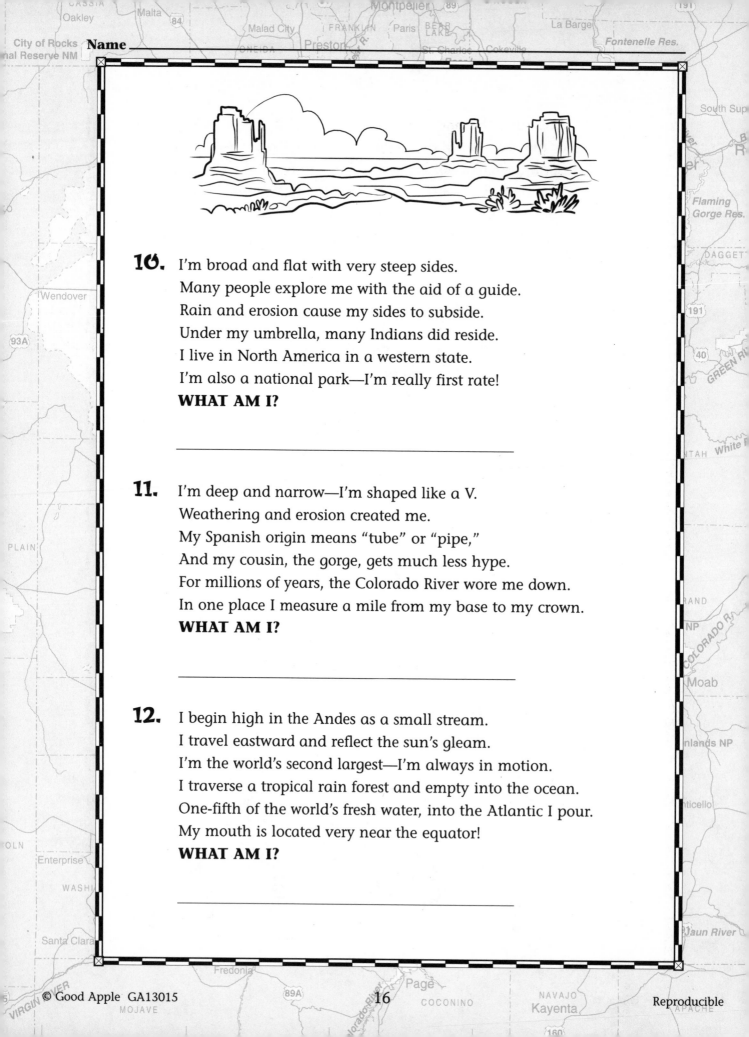

10. I'm broad and flat with very steep sides.
Many people explore me with the aid of a guide.
Rain and erosion cause my sides to subside.
Under my umbrella, many Indians did reside.
I live in North America in a western state.
I'm also a national park—I'm really first rate!
WHAT AM I?

_____

11. I'm deep and narrow—I'm shaped like a V.
Weathering and erosion created me.
My Spanish origin means "tube" or "pipe,"
And my cousin, the gorge, gets much less hype.
For millions of years, the Colorado River wore me down.
In one place I measure a mile from my base to my crown.
WHAT AM I?

_____

12. I begin high in the Andes as a small stream.
I travel eastward and reflect the sun's gleam.
I'm the world's second largest—I'm always in motion.
I traverse a tropical rain forest and empty into the ocean.
One-fifth of the world's fresh water, into the Atlantic I pour.
My mouth is located very near the equator!
WHAT AM I?

_____

13. I'm a narrow passage of water connecting an ocean and a sea.
Strategically, one is more powerful, so it controls me.
My narrow body separates Africa and Spain.
My link to the Atlantic has been of great gain.
I have many brothers such as Messina and Hormuz.
I'm found barely in the Eastern Hemisphere, if a map you peruse.
WHAT AM I?

_____

14. I'm a body of water sheltered by a natural barrier.
Into my refuge sails many an ocean carrier.
I'm one of the finest with small tidal variations.
I have very deep water and little current fluctuation.
As you cross from Manhattan to Staten, you will see
That Lady Liberty welcomes all who visit me.
WHAT AM I?

_____

15. I'm arid and dry, subtropical in kind.
In my landscape, an oasis is hard to find.
I'm crossed by the tropic of Cancer and receive little rain.
My vastness and heat can inflict immense pain.
I'm the largest hot one in the Eastern Hemisphere.
The Mediterranean Sea is fairly near to me here.
WHAT AM I?

_____

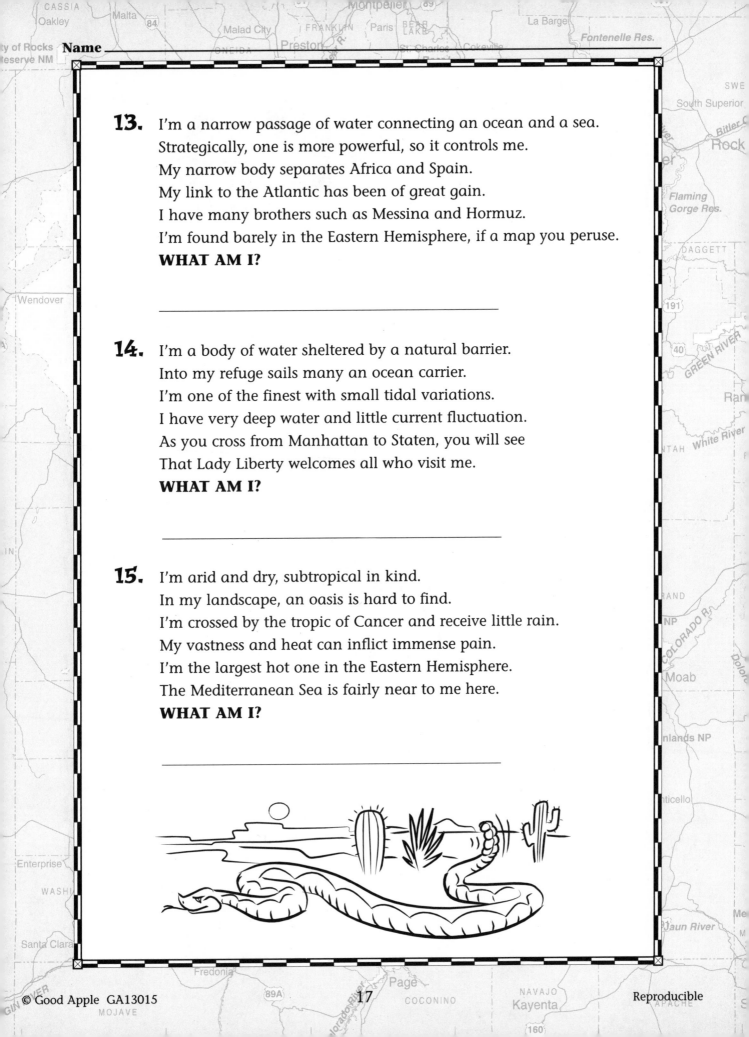

16. I'm an underground chamber in New Mexico.
Many visit me yearly—then off they go!
My 21-mile-long passages are like a maze.
At my stalactites, many curious visitors gaze.
It's very dark inside me without a light.
The bats that inhabit me can give folks a fright!
WHAT AM I?

_____

17. I'm a large body of water
Completely surrounded by land.
My area is 371,000 square kilometers;
By "lake" standards, I'm grand.
I'm located in the Eastern Hemisphere
Between two other landforms like me.
You can stand on my shore in Iran
And the former Soviet Union, you see.
WHAT AM I?

_____

18. I'm a long, narrow inlet reaching far inland from the sea.
I form in U-shaped valleys—glaciers carved the way for me.
I form a natural harbor—my sides are long and steep.
I'm the most famous one in Norway—my walls are 3,280 feet deep.
WHAT AM I?

_____

19. As I die, I leave behind a colored bony legacy.

I grow very slowly—the ocean's floor is where I'll be.

1,250 miles is the length some have measured me.

I'm shaped like branches and fans, and have cousins in the
   Florida Keys.

I'm the greatest natural barrier between the ocean and the land
   "down under."

My rough calcium-carbonated edges can tear a ship asunder!

WHAT AM I?

20. The state of California is where I can be found.

When I'm most destructive, I'm accompanied by sound.

I'm a break in Earth's crust; plate movement occurs along me.

Earthquakes often result wherever I happen to be!

WHAT AM I?

21. I'm a huge landmass whose inhabitants are diverse.

I contain the world's longest river; in its waters you can immerse.

The world's largest hot desert spans the northern part of me,

And a portion of my border is the Mediterranean Sea.

The equator dissects me, but nearby many people seek

To climb Mt. Kilimanjaro, my highest mountain peak.

WHAT AM I?

22. My bowl-like shape leaves me depressed.
Near Winslow, Arizona, is the place where I rest.
I'm found on the earth, but others like me
Are found on the moon where I'd like to be.
A major high-speed force from outer space
Has left its impression on the earth's face.
WHAT AM I?

_____

23. I'm a body of water that can vary greatly in size.
I'm one of the highest in the world—in the mountains, you
   may surmise.
You'll find me in South America—floating "islands" are
   made from my reeds.
Indians live on these islands, and I supply their every need!
WHAT AM I?

_____

24. Groundwater saturates me and soaks me right through.
From an airplane window, my wide expanse you can view.
I support many plants and animals in my grassy habitat,
Where ducks, turtles, and snakes manage to grow rather fat!
I live in southern Florida close to the Atlantic Coast.
"I'm a unique national park" is my primary boast!
WHAT AM I?

_____

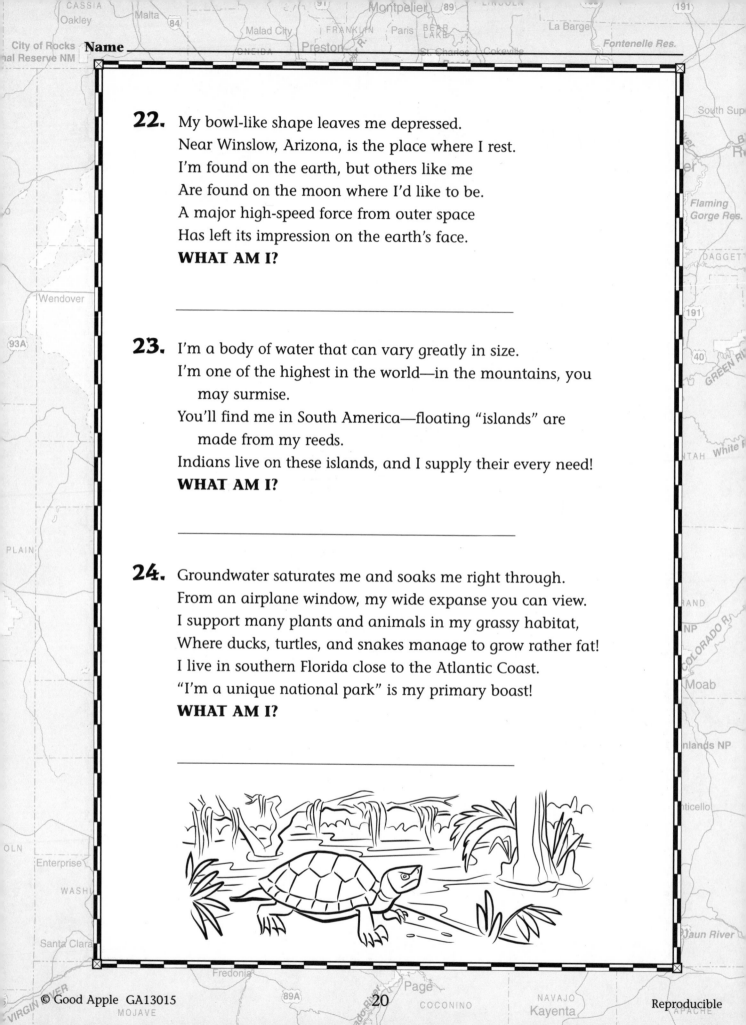

25. Inside my quiet refuge it's shady and cool.
I need 30 inches yearly rainfall—that's the "geographic rule."
My relatives are on most continents, and my foliage shades the ground.
Antarctica is the only landmass where I cannot be found.
I'm located in California—I stand tall, above the rest.
In my outstretched arms, you will often find a nest!
WHAT AM I?

_____

26. From my mouth I spew hot water from inside the earth.
Magma heats me up HOT—every hour I rebirth.
Pressure makes me explode and eject water into the air.
Thousands of visitors gaze at me, for I am unusually rare.
I'm in a northwestern state—in a national park I reside.
When I explode toward the sky, amazement you cannot hide!
WHAT AM I?

_____

27. I'm in the Southwest, once covered by a tropical sea.
My peaks were part of a reef, but erosion uncovered me.
In the walls of my cliffs are fossils of marine animals and plants.
In my highlands you may view black bears and elk, by chance.
One of my peaks, El Capitan, stands like a sentry guarding the plains,
Overlooking the Chihuahuan Desert, which receives little rain.
I'm rugged and hearty, and my silhouette stands bold.
Through my peaks and my valleys, my history is told!
WHAT AM I?

_____

© Good Apple GA13015
Reproducible

28. I'm the white-capped monarch of the Pacific Northwest.
I stand 14,400 feet tall from my base to my crest.
I'm a dormant volcano; 27 glaciers are my shrouds.
I look regal and majestic with my head above the clouds.
You can view me from Tacoma or on the islands of Puget Sound.
In the state of Washington is where I can be found.
WHAT AM I?

29. I'm one of the most unusual parks in the U.S. where I'm found.
Upon your very first view, my presence will truly astound!
I'm carved into granite by wedges, hammers, and dynamite.
I'm the largest carved figure in the world—a truly spectacular sight!
It took sculptors 14 years to carve me in Dakota's Black Hills,
But it was worth the labor and cost to give my visitors such thrills!
WHAT AM I?

30. I'm the reverse of a volcano—mountain turned inside out.
In my deep, blue waters, you'll find salmon and trout.
I'm the deepest body of water; in North America I'm found.
Wizard Island, a volcanic cone, is land my water surrounds.
I'm located in Oregon in the Cascade Range.
The Klawath Indians thought me mystical and strange.
I reflect the mountains around me, pristine and pure.
My depth, size, and beauty entice visitors with allure.
WHAT AM I?

Logic Puzzles

In the following puzzles, students try to match items that go together (O) and cross out items that do not match (X). Some puzzles are single grid, some are double grid, and some are triple grid. Students may use geography resources to help them with information given in the clues. For example, a student may use a map or globe to locate latitude, longitude, and hemisphere to determine which country is on a particular continent, but he or she should not look up the country in an encyclopedia just to find the continent.

Next, students will write "proof statements" that support their conclusions. Proof statements can be abbreviated using symbols: **=** (equals); **≠** (does not equal); .·. (therefore).

If a clue proves that two things match, an O is placed on the matrix where the two items intersect. If a clue proves that two things do not match, an X is placed on the matrix where the two items intersect. When a match is made and an O is placed on the matrix, the rest of that vertical column and horizontal row become X's.

In a double or triple matrix, individual matrices can be combined with other matrices to provide additional information. In some logic puzzles, the combining of information is essential to the solution of the problem.

Work the first logic problem with students and show them how to combine clues and write a proof statement. You may want to use an overhead so everyone in the class can see how to correctly complete the matrix. The first logic puzzle is shown below.

Rivers and States

	Arkansas River	Snake River	Tennessee River	Missouri River
Kansas	O	X	X	X
Alabama	X	X	O	X
South Dakota	X	X	X	O
Idaho	X	O	X	X

Proof Statement:

1. Idaho and Alabama ≠ Missouri River and Arkansas River
   Kansas and South Dakota ≠ Snake River and Tennessee River .·.

2. Snake River ≠ Alabama, Kansas, and South Dakota .·. Snake River = Idaho

3. Kansas and Alabama ≠ Missouri River

Rivers and States

Use the following clues and a United States map to determine which rivers flow through which states. Use the clues to prove each answer, then write a proof statement supporting your conclusions.

Clues

1. The two states bordered on the north by Tennessee and Montana do not have rivers that begin with *A* or *M*.

2. The Snake River is not in a state located between 80 degrees W and 105 degrees W.

3. The states located south of 40 degrees N do not have a river beginning with the letter *M*.

	Arkansas River	Snake River	Tennessee River	Missouri River
Kansas				
Alabama				
South Dakota				
Idaho				

© Good Apple GA13015

Reproducible

Continents and Islands

There are seven continents on the planet Earth. Several islands are located near each continent. Use the following clues and a world map and/or atlas to match the continents with their nearby islands. Write a proof statement supporting your conclusions.

Clues

1. The Bahamas, Shetlands, and New Siberian Islands are located north of the tropic of Cancer.

2. The Canary Islands are located at 27 degrees N and 16 degrees W.

3. The Shetland Islands aren't located in the Southern or Western Hemispheres; nor are they located near the two continents immediately west of the international date line.

4. The Ross Islands are located near a continent that is completely south of the tropic of Capricorn.

5. The islands located at 25 degrees N and 78 degrees W are nearest North America.

6. New Guinea is located in the Pacific Ocean between the equator and the 15th Parallel S.

Continents

Islands	North America	South America	Europe	Asia	Africa	Australia	Antarctica
Bahamas							
Falkland							
Canary							
New Guinea							
Shetland							
Ross							
New Siberian							

Cities, Countries, and Continents

In the grid on page 27 you are given the names of five cities located in five countries on five different continents. Use the clues below to match each city with the appropriate country and continent. Write a proof statement supporting your conclusions.

Clues

1. The cities north of the equator are not Perth or Maun; neither are they located in Australia or Africa.

2. Helsinki, Maun, and Aldan are east of the prime meridian.

3. Colombia is located in South America in the Western Hemisphere.

4. This city in Africa is not located at 31 degrees S and 116 degrees E, but it is north of the tropic of Capricorn.

5. Aldan is not on the continents of South America or Africa; nor is it in Australia.

6. The continent on which Botswana is located does not border the Pacific Ocean.

7. The capital of Colombia is Bogota, and it is located in the Western Hemisphere.

8. Maun is located in a country and continent whose names begin with one of the first three letters of the alphabet.

9. Finland is not in Asia, but it is north of the tropic of Cancer; the capital is 61 degrees N and 25 degrees E.

© Good Apple GA13015

Reproducible

Cities, Countries, and Continents

Cities	Countries					Continents				
	Australia	Colombia	Finland	Former U.S.S.R.	Botswana	Africa	Australia	Europe	Asia	South America
Perth										
Maun										
Helsinki										
Aldan										
Bogota										
Africa										
Australia										
Europe										
Asia										
South America										

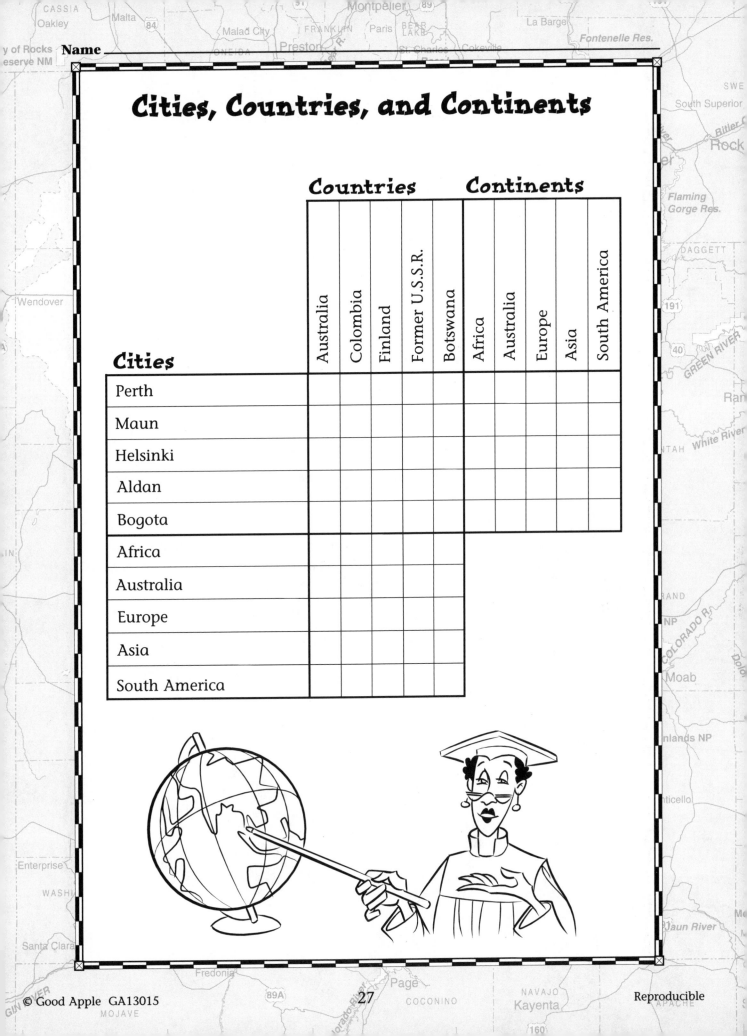

© Good Apple GA13015 Reproducible

Volcanoes

Use the following clues to determine the height of each volcano and the country in which it is located. In the grid on page 29, you are given the names of six volcanoes located in five different countries. Use the clues below to match each volcano with its height and the appropriate country. Write a proof statement supporting your conclusions.

Clues

1. Kilimanjaro is an extinct volcano with two peaks. It is not located on an island, but it is one of the three tallest mountains, and coffee is grown on its slopes.

2. Mt. Fuji is an inactive composite volcano located on an island, but not in the United States. It's the highest mountain on this island, over 12,000 feet high. It is considered to be a sacred mountain, and over 50,000 pilgrims climb to the top each year.

3. These volcanoes in Mexico and Africa are the two tallest mountains, but they are not Mt. Rainier or Mt. Etna.

4. This volcano in Sicily is still active, though it is the shortest of six mountains. It has erupted at least 260 times. The first recorded eruption was in 700 B.C., and the last eruption occurred in 1983.

5. The top of Popocatepetl is always covered with snow. It is still active, and the name the Aztecs gave it means "smoking mountain." It is one of the highest peaks in North America, yet it is located south of the tropic of Cancer.

6. Mt. Rainier is located in an American national park. Its glacial valleys cascade into beautiful streams and waterfalls on this 14,410-foot mountain peak.

7. The tallest mountain in Africa has glaciers. It is known in literature because of Hemingway's short story "The Snows of . . . ."

8. Mauna Kea is a volcano located in Hawaii. It is less than 19,000 feet high but more than 13,000 feet high.

Volcanoes

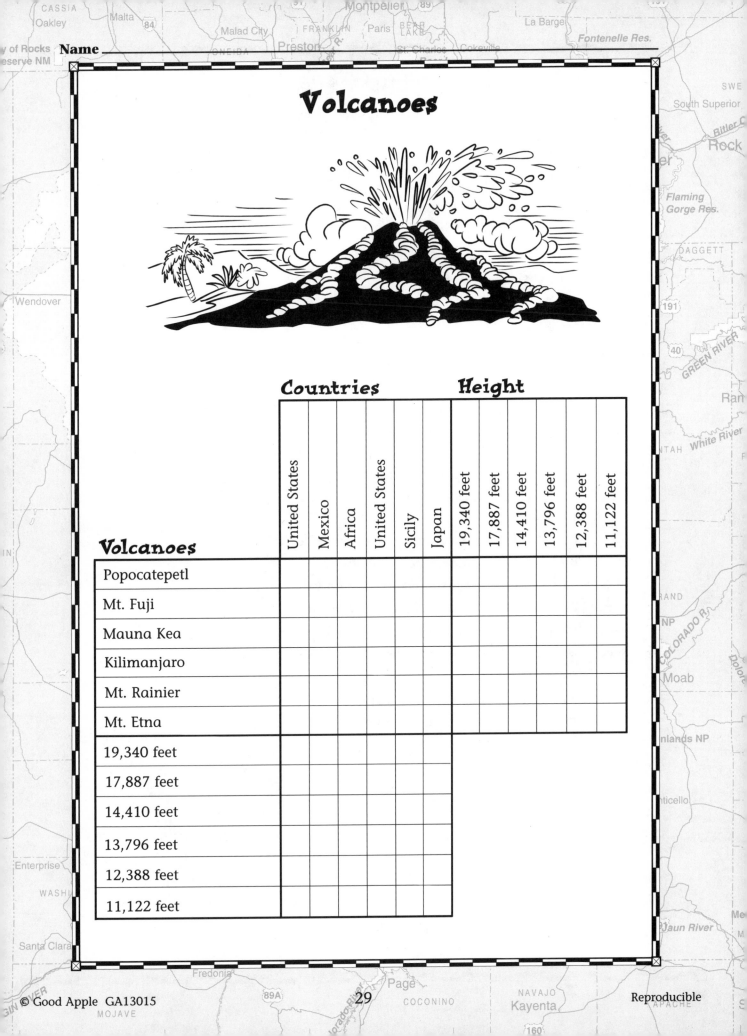

Volcanoes	Countries						Height					
	United States	Mexico	Africa	United States	Sicily	Japan	19,340 feet	17,887 feet	14,410 feet	13,796 feet	12,388 feet	11,122 feet
Popocatepetl												
Mt. Fuji												
Mauna Kea												
Kilimanjaro												
Mt. Rainier												
Mt. Etna												
19,340 feet												
17,887 feet												
14,410 feet												
13,796 feet												
12,388 feet												
11,122 feet												

© Good Apple GA13015

Reproducible

Answers

Word Wackies: States (page 7)

1. Alaska	2. Minnesota	3. Rhode Island	4. Tennessee
5. Idaho	6. Arkansas	7. North Dakota	8. Ohio
9. Connecticut	10. Washington	11. Mississippi	12. Arizona
13. Michigan	14. West Virginia	15. Colorado	16. Illinois

Word Wackies: Cities (page 8)

1. Tucson	2. Mobile	3. Columbus	4. Dover
5. Tallahassee	6. El Paso	7. Sacramento	8. Paris
9. Little Rock	10. Denver	11. Tokyo	12. Las Vegas
13. Concord	14. Florence	15. Bombay	16. Toronto

Geography Analogies: United States (page 9)

1. Austin: Montgomery and Austin are capitals of their states.

2. Mississippi River: Both rivers flow through the given cities.

3. Santa Fe: Both cities are capitals of the given states.

4. Gulf of Mexico or Atlantic Ocean: Both states rest next to this ocean or body of water.

5. Carson City: Both cities are capitals of the given states.

6. Georgia: Both are states east of the given states.

7. United States: Both are countries north of the given countries.

8. Columbia: Both cities are capitals of the given states.

9. New Hampshire: All are state(s) bordering the given states.

10. Okeechobee: Both are the largest lakes in the given states.

Geography Analogies: World (page 10)

1. Paris: Madrid and Paris are their country's capitals.

2. Spain: Both are westward neighboring countries.

3. Vietnam: Both are eastward neighboring countries.

4. Suez Canal: Both are international shipping canals.

5. Venezuela: Both countries are surrounded by the given countries.

6. Paraguay: Both are small neighboring countries to the south of the given countries.

7. Baja California: Both are the given continent's southern peninsula.

8. South America: Both are the southern-most countries on their continents.

9. Lake Superior: Both are the largest lakes on their continents.

10. Amazon River: Both are the longest rivers on their continents.

Answers

Which One Does Not Belong? United States (page 11)

1. Iowa: All other states border Wyoming.
2. Wisconsin: All other states border Canada.
3. Nevada: All other states border an ocean.
4. Nevada: All other states have a common border.
5. Louisiana: All other states border Mexico.
6. Nevada: All other states are east of the Continental Divide.
7. Ohio: All other states are bordered by the Mississippi River.
8. Alabama: All other states are on the eastern seaboard (bordered by the Atlantic Ocean).
9. Oregon: All other states are landlocked.
10. Vermont: All other states border the Great Lakes.

Which One Does Not Belong? World (page 12)

1. Panama: All other countries are in South America.
2. Paraguay: It is the only landlocked country and doesn't touch an ocean.
3. Madagascar: It is the only island country.
4. North America: All others are in the Eastern Hemisphere.
5. Antarctica: All others are oceans (Antarctica is a continent).
6. Mexico: All other countries have an ocean bordering their northern coasts.
7. Zaire: All others touch an ocean—Zaire is landlocked.
8. Vietnam: All others border the equator.
9. Hawaii: All others are countries—Hawaii is a state.
10. Arctic: All others are continents—the Arctic is an ocean.

Geography Riddles (pages 13–22)

1. Volcano: Mauna Loa
2. Bay: Chesapeake Bay
3. Isthmus of Panama
4. Delta: Mississippi Delta
5. Cape: Cape Good Hope
6. Mountain: Mt. Everest
7. Dam: Hoover Dam (Boulder)
8. Island: Madagascar
9. Yucatan Peninsula
10. Mesa: Mesa Verde
11. Canyon: Grand Canyon
12. River: Amazon River
13. Strait: Strait of Gibraltar
14. Harbor: New York Harbor
15. Desert: Sahara Desert
16. Cave: Carlsbad Caverns
17. Sea: Caspian Sea
18. Fjord: Sognefjorden Fjord
19. Reef: Great Barrier Reef
20. Fault: San Andreas Fault
21. Continent: Africa
22. Crater: Meteor Crater
23. Lake: Lake Titicaca
24. Everglades National Park
25. Redwood National Park
26. Geyser: Old Faithful
27. Guadalupe Mountains
28. Mt. Rainier National Park
29. Mt. Rushmore National Park
30. Crater Lake National Park

Answers

	Arkansas River	Snake River	Tennessee River	Missouri River
Kansas	O	X	X	X
Alabama	X	X	O	X
South Dakota	X	X	X	O
Idaho	X	O	X	X

Logic Puzzles:
Rivers and States (page 24)
Kansas = Arkansas River
Alabama = Tennessee River
South Dakota = Missouri River
Idaho = Snake River

Continents

Islands	North America	South America	Europe	Asia	Africa	Australia	Antarctica
Bahamas	O	X	X	X	X	X	X
Falkland	X	O	X	X	X	X	X
Canary	X	X	X	X	O	X	X
New Guinea	X	X	X	X	X	O	X
Shetland	X	X	O	X	X	X	X
Ross	X	X	X	X	X	X	O
New Siberian	X	X	X	O	X	X	X

Logic Puzzles:
Continents and Islands (page 25)
Bahamas = North America
Falkland = South America
Canary = Africa
New Guinea = Australia
Shetland = Europe
Ross = Antarctica
New Siberian = Asia

	Countries					Continents				
Cities	Australia	Colombia	Finland	Former U.S.S.R.	Botswana	Africa	Australia	Europe	Asia	South America
Perth	O	X	X	X	X	X	O	X	X	X
Maun	X	X	X	X	O	O	X	X	X	X
Helsinki	X	X	O	X	X	X	X	O	X	X
Aldan	X	X	X	O	X	X	X	X	O	X
Bogota	X	O	X	X	X	X	X	X	X	O
Africa	X	X	X	X	O					
Australia	O	X	X	X	X					
Europe	X	X	O	X	X					
Asia	X	X	X	O	X					
South America	X	O	X	X	X					

Logic Puzzles:
Cities, Countries, and Continents
(pages 26 and 27)
Perth = Australia = Australia
Maun = Botswana = Africa
Helsinki = Finland = Europe
Aldan = Former U.S.S.R. = Asia
Bogota = Colombia = South America

	Countries						Height					
Volcanoes	United States	Mexico	Africa	United States	Sicily	Japan	19,340 feet	17,887 feet	14,410 feet	13,796 feet	12,388 feet	11,122 feet
Popocatepetl	X	O	X	X	X	X	X	O	X	X	X	X
Mt. Fuji	X	X	X	X	X	O	X	X	X	X	O	X
Mauna Kea	X	X	X	O	X	X	X	X	X	O	X	X
Kilimanjaro	X	X	O	X	X	X	O	X	X	X	X	X
Mt. Rainier	O	X	X	X	X	X	X	X	O	X	X	X
Mt. Etna	X	X	X	X	O	X	X	X	X	X	X	O
19,340 feet	X	X	O	X	X							
17,887 feet	X	O	X	X	X							
14,410 feet	O	X	X	X	X							
13,796 feet	X	X	X	O	X							
12,388 feet	X	X	X	X	X	O						
11,122 feet	X	X	X	X	O	X						

Logic Puzzles:
Volcanoes (pages 28 and 29)
Popocatepetl = Mexico = 17,887 feet
Mt. Fuji = Japan = 12,388 feet
Mauna Kea = United States = 13,796 feet
Kilimanjaro = Africa = 19,340 feet
Mt. Rainier = United States = 14,410 feet
Mt. Etna = Sicily = 11,122 feet